MEG CABOT

The
Princess Diaries 4

Retold by Anne Collins

PRE-INTERMEDIATE LEVEL

Founding Editor: John Milne

The Macmillan Readers provide a choice of enjoyable reading materials for learners of English. The series is published at six levels – Starter, Beginner, Elementary, Pre-intermediate, Intermediate and Upper.

Level control
Information, structure and vocabulary are controlled to suit the students' ability at each level.

The number of words at each level:

Starter	about 300 basic words
Beginner	about 600 basic words
Elementary	about 1100 basic words
Pre-intermediate	about 1400 basic words
Intermediate	about 1600 basic words
Upper	about 2200 basic words

Vocabulary
Some difficult words and phrases in this book are important for understanding the story. Some of these words are explained in the story and some are shown in the pictures. From Pre-intermediate level upwards, words are marked with a number like this: ...³. These words are explained in the Glossary at the end of the book.

Answer keys
Answer keys for the *Points for Understanding* and the *Exercises* sections can be found at www.macmillanenglish.com

Contents

A Note About the Author and This Story

Meg Cabot (Meggin Patricia Cabot) was born in Bloomington, Indiana, U.S.A. She lives in New York City with her husband, Benjamin, and her cat, Henrietta. Meg Cabot studied Art at Indiana University. Then she became an illustrator of books and magazines.

Meg's first novel, *Where Roses Grow Wild*, was published in 1988. She wrote this book using the name Patricia Cabot. Her favorite authors are Jane Austen, Judy Blume, and Barbara Cartland. Her favorite food is pizza.

Some of Meg Cabot's stories are: *The Princess Diaries* (2000), *The Princess Diaries: Take Two* (2000), *The Princess Diaries: Third Time Lucky* (2001), *The Princess Diaires: Mia Goes Forth* (2002), *The Princess Diaries: Give Me Five* (2003). The Princess Diaries series has been made into two movies—*The Princess Diaries* and *The Princess Diaries 2: Royal Engagement* (Buena Vista/Walt Disney Pictures, 2001/2004).

email a way of sending messages from one computer to another.

chatrooms you can have a conversation in an Internet chatroom.

online using a computer to talk to people on a computer network, and to search for information on the Internet.

Instant Message communicating with someone directly over the Internet and replying to their messages as soon as they arrive.

text message a written message that you send or receive using a mobile phone.

4

The People in This Story

Grandmere (Clarisse Marie Renaldo)

Philippe Renaldo

Helen Thermopolis

Frank Gianini

Mia (Amelia) Thermopolis
Fat Louie

Doctor Moscovitz

Doctor Moscovitz

Lilly Moscovitz

Michael Moscovitz

Prince Pierre René Grimaldi Roberto

Boris Pelkowski

Tina Hakim Baba

Mr Weinberger

Mrs Weinberger

Contessa Elena Trevanni

Lana Weinberger

Shameeka Taylor

Principal Gupta

Lars

1

In Genovia

Saturday, January 2nd. Royal Genovian Bedroom

My name is Mia Thermopolis and I'm fourteen years old. A few months ago, my mom gave me a diary because she wanted me to write down my feelings. So now I write about everything that happens to me in this diary.

I live in New York with my mom, Helen, and my cat, Fat Louie. Three months ago, my mom married Mr Gianini—he's my Algebra[1] teacher at school. So Mr Gianini became my stepfather[2] and he lives with us too. Now my mom is pregnant[3]— she's going to have a baby in a few months' time.

I'm a freshman—a ninth grade student—at the Albert Einstein High School in New York City. At the moment, it's the Winter Break from school. But I'm not spending my vacation in New York. I'm spending it in Genovia. Genovia is a small country in Europe, near the border of France and Italy.

I'm staying here because I'm the Princess of Genovia. My full name is Her Royal Highness Princess Amelia Mignonette Grimaldi Thermopolis Renaldo. My dad is Prince Philippe, the Prince of Genovia.

My mom and dad weren't married when I was born. My mom didn't want to marry my dad because she didn't want

7

me to grow up in the palace in Genovia. So she became a single parent and looked after me without anyone's help. But although my mom and dad weren't in love with each other, they stayed friends. My dad sent money to my mom and me from Genovia, and I visited Genovia every summer.

But a few months ago my dad got cancer[4]. He had an operation and the doctors cut the cancer out of his body. Then he had chemotherapy[5] treatment. The chemotherapy worked well but now my dad is sterile—he can't have any more children. So now I'm my dad's heir[6]. When he dies, I'll become the ruler of Genovia.

I'm staying in Genovia with my dad and Grandmere, my dad's mother. Grandmere is the Dowager[7] Princess of Genovia. She speaks French, drinks cocktails[7] and smokes a lot of cigarettes. Many people are frightened of Grandmere. Sometimes I'm frightened of her too, but at other times she just makes me mad.

This is my first official visit to Genovia. To prepare for it, Grandmere gave me "princess lessons"—she taught me how to speak and act like a princess.

My best friend at the Albert Einstein High School is Lilly Moscovitz. Lilly has an older brother named Michael. I've been in love with Michael for a long time, but I didn't think he was in love with me. Then last week, at the Winter Dance at school, a wonderful thing happened. Michael told me that he was in love with me too.

But the next day, I had to leave New York and come to Genovia.

I can't stop thinking about Michael Moscovitz.

But it's OK for me to think about him. BECAUSE HE IS MY BOYFRIEND NOW!!!!!!!

Tuesday, January 5th. Royal Apartment of the Dowager Princess

Grandmere is talking to me. But I'm not really listening to her. I'm thinking about Michael.

My life in Genovia is busy but it's also very boring. I really want to call Michael or Lilly, but I can't. They're spending the Winter Break at their grandmother's house in Florida, and I don't know the phone number.

The royal palace in Genovia is very old. It was built in the 1600s. I want to email my friends but I can't because there is no Internet connection in the palace.

Most people living in the castle are older than me. The only person near to my own age is my cousin, Prince René.

René isn't really my cousin, he's a distant relation from another part of my family. He is four years older than me and he goes to a business school in France. But he doesn't work very hard. He spends most of his time driving around in his Alfa Romeo sports car, or swimming in the palace pool.

So that's my life in Genovia. I really just want to go home. I want to see Michael, my new boyfriend. I haven't even gone out on a date with him yet. I haven't been out with him as his girlfriend.

I'm in my castle in Genovia, and Michael's in his grandmother's place in Florida. It's been eighteen days since I spoke to him. I'm worried that he's forgotten me. Eighteen days is a long time. Perhaps he's met another girl in Florida— a beautiful girl with long hair and a golden tan[9].

"Amelia!" Grandmere just shouted at me. "Are you listening to me? I don't know what's wrong with you. You're not thinking about *that boy*, are you?"

Grandmere has started calling Michael *that boy*.

"If you are talking about Michael Moscovitz," I said, "then yes, I *am* thinking about him."

"You'll soon forget about him," said Grandmere.

"Amelia!" Grandmere shouted at me. "Are you listening to me? You're not thinking about *that boy, are* you?"

But Grandmere is wrong. I've loved Michael for about eight years, so I'm not going to forget him easily.

It's thirteen more days until I see the lights of New York and Michael's dark brown eyes again.

Friday, January 8th, 2 a.m., Royal Genovian Bedroom

I've just had a terrible thought.

When Michael said he loved me at the Winter Dance, perhaps he didn't mean he loved me as a girlfriend. Perhaps he only loves me as a friend.

It's the middle of the night and I should be asleep. I have a very busy day tomorrow. I have to visit the new children's part of the Prince Philippe Hospital in the morning.

But how can I sleep when my boyfriend could be falling in love with another girl? I've seen TV programs about girls in Florida. They're very beautiful.

Why am I so stupid? When Michael said that he loved me, why didn't I ask him what he meant? Why didn't I ask him, "Do you love me as a friend, or as a partner for life?"

I am never going to be able to sleep now. There is only one thing I can do. I have to call the only person who might be able to help me. That's my good friend, Tina Hakim Baba. Tina knows a lot about romance. She'll be able to tell me what to do.

Tina has gone skiing for the Winter Break, but she has her own cell phone. I have a phone here in my room.

I'll call her right now.

Friday, January 8th, 3 a.m., Royal Genovian Bedroom

Tina answered the phone. She wasn't out skiing because she hurt her foot yesterday. She was in her room, watching TV.

"Tina," I said. "I'm worried that Michael just thinks of me as a friend, not a girlfriend."

11

"What?" said Tina in a shocked voice. "But I thought you said he used 'the L word' —*Love*—on the night of the Winter Dance."

"He did," I replied. "But he didn't say that he was in love with me. He only said he loved me."

"Guys[10] only say the word if they mean it. My boyfriend never says it to me," Tina said sadly.

"But *how* did Michael mean it?" I said. "I mean, I've heard him say that he loves his dog. But he's not *in love* with his dog."

"I see," said Tina. "So what are you going to do?"

"That's why I'm calling you," I answered. "Please help me."

So then Tina thought of a plan. She was very shocked when I told her that Michael and I had not spoken since the night of the Winter Dance. I explained that I couldn't call him because I didn't know the number of his grandmother's house in Florida.

Tina said that wasn't a problem. She told me to call her back in five minutes. When I did, she had the number.

"How did you get it?" I asked in surprise.

"It was easy," she said. "I called the telephone information service. Then I asked for the number of every person named Moscovitz in the town where Michael's grandmother lives. I called each number on the list until I got the right one. Lilly answered. She's expecting you to call her."

Then Tina gave me the number. I was very happy that she had got it for me.

"So how are you going to find out if Michael is in love with you?" asked Tina.

"Well," I said. "Maybe I can just ask him, 'Michael, do you like me as a friend, or do you like me as a girlfriend?'"

"Mia," Tina said, "I don't think you should do that. Boys don't like to talk about their feelings."

"So what do you think I should do?" I asked.

"Wait until you get back to New York," said Tina. "You can only find out what a boy is feeling by looking into his eyes. He'll never tell you anything on the phone. Why don't you just ask Lilly? And then call me back. I want to know what she says."

"OK," I said.

Then I dialled the number that Tina had given me. I was so nervous that my fingers were shaking. I was going to talk to Michael—Michael, whom I'd loved for years and years and who was now my boyfriend. What was I going to say?

2

Calling Michael

Lilly answered the phone. Our conversation went like this:

LILLY: (sounding cross): I thought that you would never call.

ME: I didn't know your grandmother's number.

LILLY: And you didn't leave me your phone number in Genovia.

ME: I don't know the number of the palace in Genovia. Lilly, please tell me something. Has Michael found another girlfriend?

LILLY: Are you crazy? First, Michael hasn't gone out of the house since we've been here. He's too busy working on his computer. So he hasn't had time to meet any girls. Secondly, he's not going to go out with another girl because he likes *you.*

ME: (almost crying with relief[11]): Really, Lilly? Are you sure?

LILLY: Yes. But I don't know why I'm being so nice to you. You didn't even remember his birthday.

"His birthday?" I shouted. "Oh, Lilly, I completely forgot!"

"Yes," Lilly said. "You did. But don't worry. I'm sure he didn't expect a card. You're too busy being the Princess of Genovia."

I felt terrible. How could I forget something as important as Michael's birthday?

"Lilly," I said. "Can I talk to Michael, please?"

"OK," said Lilly. Then I heard her shout, "Michael! Phone!"

After a time, I heard some footsteps. Then Michael picked up the phone.

"Hello?" he said in a curious voice. Lilly hadn't told him who was on the phone.

When I heard Michael's voice, I felt wonderful. I forgot that it was two o'clock in the morning. I forgot that I hated my life in Genovia.

"Michael," I said. "It's me."

"Mia," he said. He sounded really happy too. "How are you?"

"I'm OK," I said. "Listen, Michael, I'm very sorry that I forgot your birthday."

Michael laughed. "That's OK," he said.

Then Michael and I had a wonderful conversation. I told him about my trip to Genovia. Then he told me about his birthday dinner with his parents and Lilly.

I was so happy listening to Michael's voice that I didn't notice how late it was.

"Isn't there a difference between the time in Genovia and the time in Florida?" asked Michael suddenly. "Isn't the

time in Genovia six hours ahead of the time in Florida? Isn't it three o'clock in the morning in Genovia?"

"Yes," I said in a dreamy voice.

"Well, you'd better go to bed," Michael said. "I'm sure you have a lot of things to do tomorrow."

"Yes," I said. "I have to go on a tour of the hospital in the morning. Then in the afternoon I have to visit the zoo."

"Mia," said Michael in a worried voice. "You'd better get some sleep. Hang up the phone and go to bed."

"You hang up first," I said.

15

"No," he said. "You hang up first."

"No," I said, very happy. "You."

"No," he said. "You."

"Both of you hang up," Lilly said very rudely over the extension[12]. "Grandma is waiting to use the phone."

So we both said goodbye very quickly, and hung up.

But I'm almost sure that Michael would have said, "I love you," if Lilly hadn't been on the line.

Sunday, January 10th, 10 a.m., Palace of Genovia

I'm really worried because I don't know what to get Michael for his birthday.

I asked Tina, and Tina said I should get him a sweater. But a sweater isn't very romantic. It's the kind of present I would get for my dad.

Tina reads a lot of romantic stories, so I was surprised that she suggested a sweater. But Tina says she asked her mom. Tina's mom used to be an international model and she dated lots of exciting men.

Tina's mom says there are rules about presents for guys. The present depends on how long you have been dating a guy.

Length of Time Going Out: Suitable Gift

1–4 months: Sweater

5–8 months: Cologne

9–12 months: Cigarette lighter (or pocket knife for a non-smoker)

1 year +: Watch

Grandmere also has a list of presents for boyfriends. Grandmere's list is like this.

Length of Time Going Out: Suitable Gift
1–4 months: Candy
5–8 months: Book
9–12 months: Handkerchief[13]
1 year +: Gloves

I don't agree with Grandmere's list at all! Who gives handkerchiefs these days? And candy? *For a guy????*

But Grandmere says her rules are the same for guys *and* girls. So Michael should only give me candy or flowers for my birthday too.

Giving a present to a boy is very difficult. Everyone has a different idea. I called my mom in New York and asked her what I should give Michael. She said boxer shorts[14].

But I can't give Michael UNDERWEAR!!!!!

Then I asked my dad. He said a pen so that Michael can write to me in Genovia. But nobody writes with a pen any more. A pen is a really boring present.

Monday, January 11th, 1 a.m., Royal Genovian Bedroom
I just got off the phone with Michael. I *had to* call him. I had to find out what he wanted for his birthday.

He says that he doesn't want anything. He says that I am the only thing he needs, and he'll see me in eight days. That will be the best present anyone could give him.

But I have to get him *something*. Something really good. But what?

I didn't call Michael just because I wanted to hear his voice. Well, perhaps I did. I've been in love with Michael for a very long time. I love the way he says my name. I love the way he laughs. I love the way he asks me what I think. It's like he really cares. And I love talking to him on the phone.

It's eight days before I can be in Michael's arms again. And I can't wait.

17

3

Jane Eyre[15]

Things were starting to go well for me at last. But then Grandmere ruined[16] everything.

I was very sleepy again today. I think Grandmere knew I was awake late last night, talking to Michael.

"I know you like *that boy*, Amelia," she said. "But there are other boys as well. You are only fourteen. You are too young to give your heart to anyone."

"I'm going to be fifteen in four months," I said. "And Juliet was only fourteen when she married Romeo."

"Well, that relationship didn't end very well, did it?" said Grandmere. "Romeo and Juliet killed themselves. Let me tell you something, Amelia. If you hope to keep *that boy*, you are doing everything wrong. You call him at every hour of the night—"

"But, Grandmere," I said. "I love him."

"But you mustn't let him know that," replied Grandmere. "If he realizes[17] how you feel, he will stop trying to please you. If you want to keep him, then stop calling him every night. Start looking at other boys. And stop thinking so much about his birthday present. He should be thinking about a birthday present for you!"

"But my birthday isn't until May," I said.

I didn't want to tell Grandmere that I had already chosen Michael's birthday present. I had taken something from the Palace Museum. But I wasn't going to tell Grandmere about *that*.

I don't feel bad about taking it from the museum. Nobody else is using it. I'm the Princess of Genovia and I own everything in that museum. Well, the royal family owns everything.

"And who says a man should only give a woman presents on her birthday?" said Grandmere. She held up her arm and I saw a huge, diamond bracelet. "Your grandfather gave this to me on March 5, 1967. That is not my birthday. He gave it to me because he thought the bracelet, like myself, was perfect. *That* is how a man should treat the woman he loves."

"I don't want Michael to give me diamonds," I said. "I just want him to ask me to the school dance."

Grandmere opened her bag and took out a book.

"Here," she said. "This is for you."

I looked at the book. "*Jane Eyre?*" I said in surprise.

"Read that book, Amelia," said Grandmere. "It will teach you a lot about relationships between men and women."

"But, Grandmere," I said.

"Read it!" Grandmere shouted.

Seven days, twenty-three hours and forty-five minutes until I see Michael again.

Tuesday, January 12th, 10 a.m. Meeting of the Genovian Parliament

Jane Eyre is very boring. Nothing exciting has happened.

19

Tuesday, January 12th, 2 p.m., Still in a Meeting of the Genovian Parliament

Jane Eyre is getting better. She has got a job as a teacher in the house of a very rich guy named Mr Rochester.

Tuesday, January 12th, 5 p.m., Still in a Meeting of the Genovian Parliament

Mr Rochester is a very sexy kind of guy.

Tuesday, January 12th, 7 p.m., Dining Room

Jane Eyre is behaving like an idiot! Something bad happened but it wasn't Mr Rochester's fault! Why is she being so mean[18] to him?

Wednesday, January 13th, 3 a.m., Royal Genovian Bedroom

I think I understand why Grandmere wanted me to read this book. But I'm not sure it's a good idea to behave like a character in a book. Especially a book written in 1846. There is a character in *Jane Eyre* named Mrs Fairfax. Mrs Fairfax warns Jane about Mr Rochester. She tells Jane not to get too friendly with Mr Rochester before they are married. She means that Jane shouldn't *chase after* Mr Rochester.

I understand this very well. It means that if I want to keep Michael, I shouldn't chase after him. So I should stop calling him so much.

But what will Michael think if I stop calling him? He might think I don't like him any more!!!!!!

It's nine o'clock at night in Florida right now. What is Michael doing? Maybe he's walking on the beach with a beautiful girl.

No, Grandmere and Mrs Fairfax are right. I mustn't call Michael. If you are always available[19], a man will lose interest in you. But if you are not always available, then men really want to see you, like in *Jane Eyre*.

Five days, ten hours and fifty-eight minutes until I see Michael again.

Thursday, January 14th, 11 p.m., Royal Genovian Bedroom

I called Tina and told her about *Jane Eyre*. Now Tina's reading it too. She agrees with me—perhaps it's not a good idea for girls to chase boys. Girls should let boys chase them. So she's decided not to email or call her boyfriend, Dave.

Then Tina and I made a promise to each other. We said that when one of us wanted to call our boyfriends, we would call each other instead.

Four days, fourteen hours and forty minutes until I see Michael again.

Saturday, January 16th, 11 p.m., Royal Genovian Bedroom

Tonight there was a royal ball[20] to celebrate the end of my first official trip to Genovia.

Grandmere has been talking about this ball all week. She kept talking about what dress she wanted me to wear, and my hair and fingernails. Now I know why she wanted me to look good. She wanted me to dance with Prince René, so that a reporter from the magazine *Newsweek* could take a photo of us.

"I will stop calling Michael so often," I told Grandmere. "But that doesn't mean I am going to start going out with Prince René."

Prince René asked me to go outside on the balcony with him because he wanted to smoke a cigarette. But I told him I don't smoke. Then I told him that I already have a boyfriend, but René just laughed.

Then my dad came up, so I told him that Grandmere was trying to fix me up[21] with Prince René. My dad went to speak to Grandmere and Prince René went away. Later, Grandmere told me that she only wanted a nice photo of Prince René and me for *Newsweek*. She thought that the photo would attract more tourists to Genovia.

Perhaps if a magazine prints the photo, Michael will see it. Then he'll be jealous like Mr Rochester was, after Jane Eyre met another man.

Two days, fourteen hours and twelve minutes before I see Michael again.

I CAN'T WAIT!!!!!!!

Monday, January 18th, 3 p.m., Genovian Time. Royal Genovian Plane. 20,000 Feet in the Air

I cannot believe that:

a. my dad is staying in Genovia. He's not coming back to New York with me

b. Grandmere said that my princess lessons have to continue and my dad agreed with her

c. Grandmere and her dog Rommel are coming back to New York with me

IT IS NOT FAIR. I went to all the princess lessons Grandmere gave me last fall[22]. I passed Algebra. I went on Genovian national TV and gave a stupid speech to the people of Genovia.

Grandmere says that I still have a lot to learn about governing a country. But I think the only reason she's coming back to New York is because she likes making my life difficult.

I don't want Grandmere to damage my relationship with Michael. I told my dad this as well. But I'm not sure that he was listening to me. He was busy watching two beautiful girls.

"Please don't tell me again that I'm too young to be in love," I said to Grandmere at lunch. "I'm old enough to know my own heart."

Michael and I are going to have a great love, just like Jane Eyre and Mr Rochester.

Twenty two hours until I see him again.

4

Home at Last

I am so happy!

I'm home!!!!! I'm home at last!!!!! I love New York. I am so happy to be home again.

When I looked out of the plane's window, and saw the bright lights of Manhattan[23] below me, I felt really good. I love New York. I was so happy to be home again.

Lars, my bodyguard, was waiting for me when I stepped off the plane. Lars' job is to look after me. He must stop anyone from trying to kidnap[24] me.

Lars looked very tanned because he has been on holiday with Wahim, Tina Hakim Baba's bodyguard. Tina's father is very rich because he owns an oil company. So Tina has a bodyguard too.

Lars drove me home. My mom was waiting for me. It was so good to see her!!!!! She looks great. She's four months pregnant now and she is starting to get bigger. It's difficult to hug her because the baby gets in the way.

"I missed you so much!" said my mom.

Mr Gianini was looking great too, he's growing a beard. Then I saw my cat, Fat Louie. I picked him up and gave him a great big hug.

The loft[25] looks wonderful. While I was away, Mr Gianini put in a special kind of Internet connection. So now I can go online without using the telephone.

But the best thing was waiting for me on the answering machine. My mom played it for me as soon as I walked in the door.

IT WAS A MESSAGE FROM MICHAEL!!!!! MY FIRST MESSAGE FROM MICHAEL SINCE I BECAME HIS GIRLFRIEND!!!!!

This is the message:

Hi, Mia. It's Michael. Please could you call me when you get this message? I'm worried because I haven't heard from you for some time. And I just wanted to know if you're OK. And if you got home all right. OK. That's all. Well. Bye...This is Michael, by the way. Or maybe I said that? I can't remember. Hi, Mrs Thermopolis. Hi, Mr G. Well. Call me, Mia. Bye.

I took the tape out of the machine and brought it into my room. I played it about fifty times. It was the best Christmas present I've ever had.

My mom kept coming into my room to give me more hugs. The last time she came in, I was playing Michael's message again.

"Haven't you called him back yet?" she asked.

"No," I said.

"Why not?" asked my mom.

"Because I'm trying to be like Jane Eyre," I said.

"Jane Eyre?" said my mom. "You mean the girl in the book?"

"That's right," I said. "Jane Eyre didn't chase boys, she let them chase her."

But my mom didn't look happy about this.

"Jane Eyre was so mean to poor Mr Rochester!" she cried.

I didn't say that this was what I had thought, too . . . at first.

"Where did you get your ideas from, Mia?" asked my mom. "Who told you about *Jane Eyre*?"

"Grandmere," I said. I knew my mom wasn't going to like that answer. Mom and Grandmere are very different people, and they don't get along very well.

"Well," said my mom. "I'm pleased that you and your friends have decided not to chase boys. However, if a nice boy like Michael leaves you a message on your answering machine, you should return his call. That's not chasing boys—that's being polite."

I thought about this. My mom was probably right.

"OK," I said. "I suppose I could return his call." Suddenly I felt very excited about speaking to Michael again.

"I don't think you should play games with boys," said my mom. "Not with a boy you like. Especially not Michael."

"Mom, if I want to spend the rest of my life with Michael, I have to play games with him," I said. "If he knows how I really feel about him, he might run away. I love Michael more than anything in the world, except for you and Dad and Fat Louie."

Actually, I think I love Michael more than I love my mom and dad. That sounds like a terrible thing to say, but it's how I feel. But I will never love anyone or anything as much as I love Fat Louie.

"It's good that you want to take things slowly with Michael," said my mom. "But if a boy you like leaves a message for you, then you should call him back. Or he might think that you don't like him any more."

Suddenly I felt very worried. Perhaps Michael had fallen in love with another girl. Perhaps he was on the phone to her right now.

"Mia," said my mom, looking worried. "Are you all right?"

I tried to smile, but I couldn't. I wanted my mom to leave the room so I could call Michael.

"Mom," I said. "I have to call Michael now."

"Oh, Mia," said my mom, looking pleased. "I really think you should. Charlotte Brontë, the author of *Jane Eyre*, was a very good writer. But things were different back in the 1840s."

Then I remembered something. Michael and Lilly's parents don't allow Michael and Lilly to use the phone after eleven o'clock on weeknights. And it was almost eleven o'clock now.

As soon as my mom had gone, I grabbed[26] the phone. But before I could pick up the receiver, it began to ring.

My heart jumped with excitement. I knew it was Michael calling. It rang again and I picked it up.

"Hello?"

But it wasn't Michael. It was Grandmere.

"Grandmere," I said. I couldn't believe it. The time was ten fifty-nine. I had one minute left to call Michael. If I didn't ring him now, I would make his parents angry.

"I can't talk now Grandmere," I said, "I have to make another call."

"Oh?" said Grandmere. "And who are you calling at this time of night?"

"Grandmere," I said. "It's OK. He called me first. I am returning his call. It's the polite thing to do."

"It's too late for you to be calling *that boy*," said Grandmere.

Now it was eleven o'clock. I had missed my chance to call Michael because of Grandmere.

27

"You'll see him at school tomorrow," said Grandmere. "Now let me speak to your mother."

This shocked me. Grandmere never usually speaks to mom. They haven't had a good relationship since my mom got pregnant and refused to marry my dad.

So I took the phone into the living room and passed it to my mom. She was watching TV with Mr Gianini. I didn't tell her that it was Grandmere on the phone.

"Hello?" I heard my mom say in a bright voice.

Then I came back to my room. I was thinking about what I would say to Michael in the morning. Then suddenly I had a brilliant[27] idea. Perhaps I could send an Instant Message to Michael on my computer. I turned it on. Michael was online! So I wrote this message to him.

```
Michael, it's me! I'm home. I wanted to call you, but
it's after eleven.  I didn't want your mom and dad to
be mad.
```

Michael has changed his online name. He used to be CracKing but now he's LinuxRulz.

```
LinuxRulz:  Welcome home! It's good to hear from you.
I was worried about you.
FtLouie: I've just been very busy. Should Lars and I
pick you and Lilly up on the way to school tomorrow?
LinuxRulz: That would be good. What are you doing on
Friday?
```

What am I doing on Friday? Was Michael asking me out on a date? I felt very excited, but I tried to type calmly.

```
FtLouie: Nothing, as far as I know. Why?
LinuxRulz: Do you want to go to dinner at the Screening
Room cinema? They're showing the first Star Wars film.
```

HE WAS ASKING ME OUT. Dinner *and* a movie. At the Screening Room you sit at a table and have dinner. You watch the movie as you eat. *Star Wars* is my favorite film. I think I am the luckiest girl in the world.

My fingers were shaking as I wrote:

FtLouie: I think that would be OK. I'll have to check with my mom. Can I let you know tomorrow?

LinuxRulz: OK. So see you tomorrow. Around 7.45?

FtLouie: Tomorrow. 7.45.

I could not imagine a more perfect date. Mom will let me go because I'm going with Michael and she thinks he's a nice boy. Even Mr Gianini likes Michael.

I'm too excited to sleep now. *I am going to see Michael in eight hours and fifteen minutes.*

5

A New Semester

Tuesday, January 19th. Algebra class

I felt terrible this morning. I was so tired that I couldn't get out of bed. I am jetlagged[28] after the long plane journey back from Genovia. I only got up because I was so excited about seeing Michael again.

I opened my underwear drawer to look for my lucky underwear. This underwear has a picture of Queen Amidala on it. Queen Amidala is the heroine[29] in the first three *Star Wars* movies. Whenever I wear this special underwear, I believe it brings me good luck. For example, I was wearing it at the Winter Dance when Michael told me he loved me.

I always wear my Queen Amidala underwear on the first day of a new semester. I wear it so that things will go well for me. But this morning my Queen Amidala underwear wasn't in my underwear drawer. So I went into my mom's room and woke her up.

"Mom, I need my Queen Amidala underwear," I said. "Where is it?" But my mom wasn't listening to what I was saying because she hadn't woken up properly.

"Shnurowog," she said, which isn't even a proper word. So then I had an idea.

"Mom, can I go for dinner with Michael at the Screening Room this Friday night?" I asked. I knew my mom wasn't really listening to me because she was still sleeping. So she wasn't going to say "no."

"Yeah, yeah," she said.

So now I had my mom's permission to go out with Michael. But I had to wear my ordinary underwear to school and I wasn't very happy about that. There's nothing special about my ordinary underwear—it's just boring and white.

Then Lars drove me to Michael and Lilly's place. I was excited about seeing Michael, but I was also worried. What was I going to say to him? I hadn't seen him for thirty-two days. How was I going to hug him in front of Lars and Lilly?

When we got to Michael and Lilly's building, I jumped out of the car. Michael was standing there, looking tall and handsome. My heart started beating very fast. When he saw me, he smiled a wonderful smile.

"Hi," I said nervously.

"Hi," Michael said. "It's really good to see you."

Lilly walked past us and got into the car.

"It's really cold," she said. "Will you two hurry up and get in?"

Michael put his hand on the car door to open it for me. But then he put his other hand on my arm. As I turned around he said,

"So can you go out with me on Friday night?"

"Yes," I replied.

Then he pulled me towards him and kissed me, in front of all the people on the street! And he kissed me in a very special and romantic way.

I got into the back of the car with Lilly. I had a big smile on my face. I thought Lilly would laugh at me, but I didn't care because I was so happy. I wasn't wearing my Queen Amidala underwear, but the new semester had started very well for me.

Then Michael got in beside me and closed the door. Lars said "Good morning" to Lilly and Michael, and they said "Good morning" back.

For the first time in my life, the guy who I like actually likes—maybe even *loves*—me too. It's a wonderful feeling.

Tuesday, January 19th. Algebra class

When I was sitting in Mr Gianini's Algebra class today, Michael came in.

I am only a freshman and Michael is a senior student. Seniors don't usually walk into freshman classes unless they have a special reason. But Michael came into the class just to see me. He came right up to my desk with his school schedule in his hand.

"What time do you have lunch?" he asked, so I told him.

"Same as me," he said. "Do you have your Special Project class[30] afterwards?"

"Yes."

"Great," he said. "See you at lunch."

Then he turned and walked out again, looking tall and cool.

I can't believe that Michael has been in to see me. ME, MIA THERMOPOLIS. I used to be the most unpopular person here. Now everyone knows that I'm going out with one of the coolest and best-looking boys in the school.

Everybody in the class was staring at me in surprise, including Lana Weinberger. Lana is beautiful, but she's always been very mean to me.

Lana got out her cell phone and started telling one of her friends about Michael's visit. But Mr Gianini doesn't allow students to use cell phones in class. He took Lana's phone away and told her to write an essay of a thousand words. The subject is: "*How rude it is to make cell phone calls during class.*"

Tuesday, January 19th. Special Project class

I am so depressed[31]. I know I shouldn't be depressed because there are many great things about my life.

Great Thing Number One

The boy I have been in love with for a long time loves, or really likes, me too. We are going out on our first real date on Friday.

Great Thing Number Two

I know it is only the first day of the new semester, but I am not flunking anything yet—I'm not failing it. Not even Algebra, which is my worst subject.

Great Thing Number Three

I am no longer in Genovia, the most boring place in the world.

Great Thing Number Four

I don't have Kenny for my Biology partner any more. Kenny used to be my boyfriend. But when I was going out with Kenny, I was really in love with Michael. Kenny has a new girlfriend now. He's going out with a girl from our Biology class. My new Biology partner is my friend, Shameeka. She's really good at science.

Great Thing Number Five

I have really cool friends who seem to like being with me, and not only because I'm a princess.

So I have all these great things in my life, and I should be really happy.

Perhaps I'm only depressed because I am feeling so tired because of the jetlag. But I can't stop feeling bad about myself.

WHAT AM I DOING IN THIS SPECIAL PROJECT CLASS?

I have no right to be in this class. I have no special talents[32], like my friends. I am not good at anything.

All my friends can do wonderful things. Lilly has her own television show. Michael can play the guitar and many other musical instruments. He can also design computer programs. Boris, Lilly's boyfriend, is brilliant at playing the violin. Tina Hakim Baba can read a book every day. Shameeka is very good at science.

But I can't do anything really well. I don't know why Michael even likes me. I am such a boring person.

As I was writing this, Lilly leaned over.

"What's wrong with you?" she asked. "You look terrible."

I told Lilly that I was depressed because I didn't have a special talent.

"They only put me in this Special Project class because I was flunking Algebra," I said.

"But you do have a talent," Lilly told me.

I stared at her. My eyes were wide with surprise.

"What is it?" I asked.

"If you don't know, I'm not going to tell you," said Lilly. "You have to guess what it is by yourself. But right now, your talent is obvious."

I looked around, but I didn't know what Lilly was talking about. I'm not talented at anything. I know Michael loves me, but that just makes things worse. Michael is good at everything, and I am not good at anything.

Tuesday, January 19th. In the Limousine[33] on the way to Grandmere's for Princess Lesson

I've made a list of things to do.

1. Find my Queen Amidala underwear.
2. Stop worrying about whether Michael is in love with me or not. Be happy with what I have. Remember, lots of girls have no boyfriends at all.
3. Call Tina to talk about how we are not chasing boys.
4. Do all homework.
5. Wrap Michael's birthday present.
6. Find out what Grandmere talked to Mom about last night.
7. Stop biting my fingernails.
8. Buy things for Fat Louie.
9. Think about a secret talent.
10. GET SOME SLEEP!!!!!! Boys don't like girls who have big ugly circles under their eyes. Not even perfect boys like Michael.

6

Grandmere's Big Lie

Wednesday, January 20th. Homeroom[34]
I was really tired yesterday. I fell asleep in the limousine on the way to my princess lesson with Grandmere. So Lars turned around and drove me home again. Then he carried me up to my room and my mom put me to bed. I slept for fifteen hours until seven o'clock this morning.

I felt much better this morning. I didn't feel depressed because I have no special talent. Not everyone can be as clever as Lilly and Michael. Not everyone can be as good at music as Boris.

It was wonderful seeing Michael again this morning.

Wednesday, January 20th. Outside Principal Gupta's Office
I am sitting here outside Principal Gupta's office. Principal Gupta has asked to see me and I don't know why. I haven't done anything wrong.

I know I didn't finish my homework, but I have a note from Mr Gianini. I gave the note to the school office this morning.

PLEASE EXCUSE MIA FOR NOT BRINGING HER HOMEWORK. SHE WAS VERY TIRED BECAUSE OF JETLAG AND COULDN'T DO HER SCHOOLWORK YESTERDAY EVENING. SHE WILL DO THE WORK TONIGHT.
FRANK GIANINI

I can hear a voice coming from Principal Gupta's office. I'm sure I know that voice. It sounds like . . . Grandmere!

Wednesday, January 20th. Grandmere's Limousine

I can't believe what Grandmere did. She told Principal Gupta a big lie and she made me feel very worried about my dad.

When Grandmere came out of Principal Gupta's office, she was talking about someone who was very ill.

"Well, we are all hoping he gets better soon," she was saying to Principal Gupta.

I felt my face go pale. Who was Grandmere talking about? Was my father sick again?

I stood up. My heart was beating very fast.

"What is it?" I said in a nervous voice. "Is it my dad? Has the cancer come back?"

"I will tell you in the car," said Grandmere in a firm voice. "Come with me."

"Don't worry about your homework, Mia," called Principal Gupta. "Just give all your attention to your father."

So it was true! Dad *was* sick!

"Is it the cancer again?" I asked Grandmere as we walked down the steps outside the school towards the limousine. "Will he have to have more chemotherapy?"

Grandmere didn't reply. When we were in the car, she turned to me.

"Really, Amelia," she said. "There's nothing wrong with your father."

I stared at Grandmere. I couldn't believe what she was saying.

"Wait a minute," I said. "You mean . . . Dad isn't sick?"

"He sounded very healthy when I spoke to him this morning," said Grandmere.

"Then what . . .?" I stared at her. "Why did you tell Principal Gupta . . .?"

"Your school principal only lets pupils out of school if the reason is very serious," said Grandmere. "So I had to tell

37

her that your father was sick. That was the only way to get you out of school for the day."

I was very shocked.

"Grandmere," I cried. "You can't just take me out of school whenever you want to. And you can't tell Principal Gupta my dad is sick when he isn't! How could you say that? If you tell a lie like that, it may become true. Perhaps Dad really will get sick."

"Don't be silly, Amelia," said Grandmere.

"Where are we going?" I asked. "We must be back at school in time for lunch. Because Michael will wonder where I am."

"Not *that boy* again," said Grandmere.

"Yes, *that boy*," I said. "The boy I'm in love with."

"Oh, we're here," said Grandmere suddenly. "Get out of the car, Amelia."

I got out and looked around. We were outside the big Chanel shop on Fifty-Seventh Avenue. But why had Grandmere brought me here?

Grandmere was walking quickly towards the big glass doors.

"Grandmere," I cried, rushing after her. "Did you take me out of school just to go shopping?"

"You need a dress," Grandmere said, "for the black-and-white ball at Contessa[35] Trevanni's this Friday evening."

"What black-and-white ball?" I asked.

"Didn't your mother tell you?" said Grandmere. "Contessa Trevanni is having a ball on Friday. It's a special ball where all the guests wear only black or white clothes."

A tall thin woman with red hair was approaching us. She was the sales lady. "Your Royal Highnesses!" she cried. "How delightful to see you!"

"My mother didn't tell me about a ball," I said to Grandmere. "When did you say it was?"

We were outside the big Chanel shop on Fifty-Seventh Avenue.

"Friday night," said Grandmere. Then she turned to the sales lady and said, "I believe you have some white dresses for my granddaughter. She's too young to wear black."

"Of course," the sales lady replied with a big smile. "Come with me, Your Highnesses."

"Friday night?" I cried. "Grandmere, I can't go to any ball on Friday night. I've already made plans with . . . ."

But Grandmere just put her hand on my back and pushed me after the sales lady.

Wednesday, January 20th. Grandmere's Limousine, on my way back to school

My mother must have given Grandmere permission to take me to this ball. Why didn't my mom tell me? Why is Contessa Trevanni having this ball? And why does Grandmere always ruin my life?

I told Grandmere I couldn't go to this ball because Michael and I are having our first date. But Grandmere told me that the first duty[36] of a princess is always to her people.

I explained that Friday night is the only night that *Star Wars* is showing at the Screening Room. But Grandmere said that my date with Michael isn't as important as Contessa Trevanni's black-and-white ball.

She told me that the Contessa is an important member of the royal family in Monaco. She is also a cousin of our family. If I don't go to the ball, the Contessa will be upset.

We're at the school. It's lunchtime. I will have to explain to Michael why I can't go on our first date.

Wednesday, January 20th. Special Project class

I couldn't tell him.

At lunch everyone was worried because they thought my father was ill. Michael was very nice to me too.

"Is there anything I can help you with?" he asked. "Your Algebra homework? I know it isn't much, but it's all I can do."

How could I tell him the truth—that my grandmother told a lie to Principal Gupta because she wanted to take me on a shopping trip?

I couldn't tell him. I sat there very quietly at lunch. Everyone thought I was worrying about my dad. But I was thinking I HATE MY GRANDMOTHER. I HATE MY GRANDMOTHER. I HATE MY GRANDMOTHER.

As soon as lunch was over, I went to one of the payphones and called home. My mom answered.

"Why didn't you tell me about the ball on Friday?" I asked.

"Oh, Mia, I'm so sorry," she said.

"Mom," I said. "Why did you tell Grandmere it was OK for me to go to this stupid ball? You said that I could go out with Michael that night!"

"I did?" said my mom in a surprised voice. She couldn't remember because she hadn't been awake when I asked her. "Oh, I am so sorry, Mia," she said. "You'll just have to cancel your date with Michael. He'll understand."

"Mom," I cried. "You've got to do something to help me!"

"Well, Mia," said my mom. "I'm surprised you're so unhappy. I thought you didn't want to chase Michael. So if you cancel your first date with him, you aren't chasing him."

"That's very funny, Mom," I said. "But Jane Eyre wouldn't cancel her first date with Mr Rochester. You've got to help me."

My mom said that she would call my dad in Genovia and talk to him about the ball. But I know what my dad will say. He'll make me go to the ball. My dad believes that duty is more important than love.

Now I am sitting here in the Special Project class. How am I going to tell Michael that our first date is canceled? Will he be so mad that he never asks me on a date again? Perhaps he'll ask another girl to go and see *Star Wars* with him!

Lilly keeps passing me little notes in the class. She has noticed how unhappy I look.

Is your dad very sick? Are you going to have to fly back to Genovia?
No, I wrote back.
Is it the cancer?
No, I wrote back.
Well, what is it, then? Why won't you tell me what's wrong?

Lilly kept writing notes, so finally I told her the truth. *Nothing's wrong*, I wrote. *Grandmere just wanted to take me shopping at Chanel, so she told Principal Gupta a lie.* *That's terrible*, Lilly wrote back.

But Lilly doesn't know about *all* the problems that Grandmere has caused. She doesn't know that I have to cancel my date with Michael on Friday.

7

A Shock for Tina

Tina Hakim Baba is very upset. She got a text message on her cell phone from her boyfriend, Dave Farouq El-Abar. The text message said,

> **U NEVER CALLED BACK.**
> **AM TAKING JASMINE TO**
> **RANGERS HOCKEY GAME.**
> **HAVE A NICE LIFE.**

That is the meanest text message I have ever read.

Lilly and I tried to say things to make Tina feel better.

"Don't worry, Tina," said Lilly. "You'll find somebody better."

But Tina wouldn't stop crying.

"I d–don't want someone b–better," she sobbed. "I only want D–Dave!"

It's terrible to see Tina in such pain. But I think I have learned a lesson from what has happened. Tina and I decided that the best way to keep our boyfriends was not to chase after them. That's why Tina stopped calling Dave. But now Dave has broken up with her.

Lilly has had her boyfriend, Boris, for a long time. She doesn't chase after him. He chases after her instead.

I must learn the secret of keeping my boyfriend. I never want to get a text from Michael like the text Tina got from Dave.

I can't cancel my date with Michael now. I am not going to that black-and-white ball. I don't care if Grandmere and Contessa Trevanni are really angry with me.

Wednesday, January 20th. In the Limousine on the Way Home from Grandmere's

Grandmere wants to destroy my love life because she doesn't like Michael. Michael makes me very happy, but Grandmere doesn't care about that. She doesn't like Michael because he isn't a member of a royal family.

How do I know this? Because when I walked into Grandmere's hotel suite today for my princess lesson, I had a big shock. Prince René was there, carrying a tennis racquet. He had just come from a tennis lesson at the New York Health Club.

"What are YOU doing here?" I asked. Grandmere told me later that I sounded very rude.

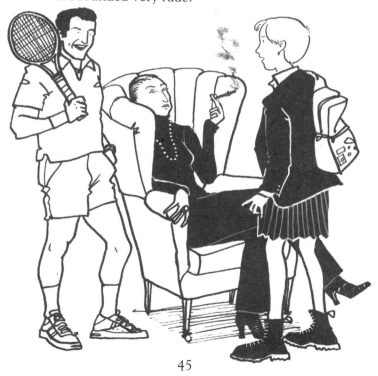

"Enjoying your beautiful city," René replied. Then he went off to have a shower.

"Really, Amelia," said Grandmere. "Is that a nice way to greet your cousin?"

"Why isn't he back in school?" I asked. Prince René was studying business at a college in France.

"He's on a break," replied Grandmere. "European schools have a longer break than American colleges. So I invited René to Manhattan. He has never been here before and he wanted to see New York—the city that never sleeps."

Then Grandmere started talking about the black-and-white ball on Friday. She said that many of the guests would be daughters of very rich and important people in New York.

Suddenly I had an idea.

Why couldn't Michael come with me to the black-and-white ball as my escort[37]? But how would I make Grandmere agree to my plan?

"About this dance, Grandmere," I said. "Do you think the Contessa would mind if I brought someone?"

Grandmere looked at me. Her dog, Rommel, was sitting on her lap and she was combing his fur.

"What do you mean?" she asked. "Do you mean you want to bring your mother? I don't think she would have a very nice time at the ball."

"Not my mom," I said. "I was thinking, you know, of an escort."

"But you already have an escort," said Grandmere. "Prince René has very kindly offered to escort you to the ball."

"*René* is going to be my escort?" I said in surprise. "*René* is taking me to the black-and-white ball?"

"Well, yes," Grandmere said. "He is a stranger to New York—and to America. You should be happy to make him feel welcome."

"Grandmere, are you trying to fix up Prince René and

me?" I asked. "First of all, you made me dance with Prince René at the ball in Genovia . . . "

"That was for a picture in a magazine," said Grandmere.

". . . and you don't like Michael . . ." I told her.

"I never said I didn't like Michael," said Grandmere. "But you're not like other girls, Amelia. You're a princess. You have to think about what is best for your country."

". . . then René comes here," I went on, "and you tell me he's taking me to the black-and-white ball."

"I just want René to have a good time while he's here," replied Grandmere.

What am I supposed to do now? About Michael, I mean? I can't take him *and* Prince René to the ball.

This new year has not started very well. First, Tina hurts her foot and loses her true love. Then I realize I have no special talent. AND now I have to go to a black-and-white ball with Prince René.

Wednesday, January 20th. The Loft

My mom came to see me while I was doing my homework in my room. She said that she still hasn't been able to speak to my dad about the black-and-white ball. He's very busy with important government business in Genovia.

"You should let Michael know," she said, "that you won't be able to go out with him on Friday."

"Mom," I said. "I don't want to say anything to Michael until we've heard from Dad. What if Michael breaks up[38] with me and then Dad says I don't have to go to the stupid ball?"

"Mia," my mom said, "Michael is not going to break up with you just because you have to do something for your family."

"Dave Farouq El-Abar broke up with Tina today because she didn't return his calls," I told her.

47

"That's different," said my mom. "It's rude if you don't return someone's calls. Let me give you some advice, Mia. If you think you may not be able to go out with Michael on Friday, you should start letting him know now. Then, when you tell him you can't go, he won't get such a shock."

"Oh," I said. "You think that if I start preparing him for bad news now, he won't dump[38] me?"

"Mia," my mom said. "No boy is going to dump you because you have to cancel a date. And if he does, then he's not the right boyfriend for you. Now do your homework."

But I couldn't concentrate on my homework because I was thinking about my mom's advice. So I went online to send Michael an Instant Message. But I found that Tina was Instant Messaging me. Tina's online name is *Iluvromance* because she loves romantic stories.

Iluvromance: Hi Mia. What are you doing?

FtLouie: I'm just doing my Biology homework. How are you?

Iluvromance: OK. But I miss him so much!!!!!!!!!!! I wish I had never even heard of Jane Eyre.

I remembered what my mom said, so I wrote:

FtLouie: Tina, if Dave broke up with you just because you didn't return his calls, then he was not the right boyfriend for you. You will find a new boy who appreciates you.

Iluvromance: Do you really think so?

FtLouie: Yes. Don't worry, we'll find someone for you. I have to go now. I have to send an instant message to my dad.

Iluvromance: OK. If you feel like chatting later, I'll be here. I have nowhere else to go.

Poor Tina. She sounded so sad. I didn't want to tell her that the person I was going to email was Michael, not my dad. I didn't want to remind her that I had a boyfriend and she didn't.

48

I think Tina's life will be much better without Dave. He didn't behave in a very kind way towards her.

I'm glad MY boyfriend is so different. Well, I hope he is different. Wait, of course he is. He's MICHAEL.

Then I emailed Michael.

FtLouie: Is there a later showing of the Star Wars movie on Friday than the seven o'clock showing?

LinuxRulz: Yes, there's a showing at eleven o'clock. Why?

This was my chance to tell Michael that I couldn't go out with him. But I couldn't tell him. I was remembering Tina and how sad she sounded. I didn't want to lose Michael. We chatted for a few minutes longer, then Michael wrote:

LinuxRulz: Do you have a princess lesson on Friday? Was that why you were asking if there was a later showing of Star Wars? Are you worried your grandmother isn't going to let you out in time for the film?

It was the perfect time to tell Michael about the ball. But I still couldn't do it. What would I do if he dumped me and found another girl to take to *Star Wars*?

So instead, I wrote:

FtLouie: No, it will be OK. I'm sure I can get out of my princess lesson early.

WHY AM I SO STUPID??? WHY DID I WRITE THAT? Because of course I won't be able to leave the stupid black-and-white ball early, I'll be there ALL NIGHT!!!!!

8

Shameeka's Surprise

Thursday, January 21st. Homeroom

This morning at breakfast, Mr Gianini asked,

"Has anyone seen my brown pants?"

Then my mom said,

"No, but has anyone seen my red T-shirt with the long sleeves?"

And then I said, "No, but I still haven't found my Queen Amidala underwear."

And that's when we realized that someone has stolen our laundry[40]. That's why I can't find my underwear.

We send our dirty clothes to a laundry on Thompson Street. When the clothes have been washed and ironed, the laundry puts them in a bag and sends them back to us. But when they deliver the bag of clothes back to our building, they leave it in the hall downstairs.

Our apartment is three flights of stairs up from the hall. So sometimes the bag stays there in the hall until one of us comes in and sees it. Then we carry it up to our apartment.

We sent a bag of dirty clothes to the laundry on the day I went to Genovia. But it hasn't come back from the laundry. So maybe someone has stolen it.

That means everyone will find out that I wear Queen Amidala underwear. Everyone will know that the Princess of Genovia has lucky Queen Amidala underwear. Perhaps the person who has stolen it will try to sell it!

Thursday, January 21st. Algebra class

Today, before class started, I heard Lana talking to a friend on her cell phone.

"I've got to go to a stupid dance on Friday evening," she was saying. "One of my dad's patients is holding it. Everyone has to dress up in black-and-white clothes."

Then I remembered that Lana's dad was a plastic surgeon—his job is to carry out medical operations[41] to make people look more attractive. He improves parts of their bodies by changing them.

I remembered Grandmere told me that Contessa Trevanni had had a facelift operation—an operation that makes a woman look younger. Had Lana's dad given Contessa Trevanni her facelift?

"This woman claims she's some kind of countess," Lana was saying to her friend on the phone. "This city is full of people who *think* they are royal."

As she said this, Lana turned round and looked at me. Her long blonde hair fell all over my Algebra book.

"No, I'm not taking Josh," she said to her friend. Josh is Lana's boyfriend and one of the best-looking boys in the school. "He is too immature," she went on. "He doesn't know how to act in a grown-up way. I'm looking forward to meeting some older boys at the dance."

I was shocked. How could Lana want to go to the ball without her boyfriend? I'm not looking forward to going to it without Michael. And it's going to be even worse if Lana is going to be there too.

Thursday, January 21st. Special Project class

Tina is mad at *Jane Eyre*. At lunchtime today, she said that *Jane Eyre* had ruined her life. She also said that she is giving up reading romantic stories because they ruined her relationship with Dave. We were all very upset when she said this. Tina *loves* reading romantic stories. She reads a new story every day.

Lilly and I wanted to show Tina that her relationship with Dave didn't end because of romantic stories. Dave caused the relationship to end, not *Jane Eyre*. So we made a list of ten romantic heroines like Juliet in *Romeo and Juliet*. After she had read our list, Tina said that we were right and romantic heroines were her friends. So she wasn't going to stop reading romantic stories.

Then my other friend, Shameeka, said,

"I'm going to apply to get onto the cheerleading team. I'm going to try and become a cheerleader[42]."

We were very surprised. Shameeka would make a very good cheerleader. She is tall and attractive and very good at dancing and gymnastics. She knows a lot about fashion and make-up too.

But Lana Weinberger and her friends are all cheerleaders. Why does Shameeka want to be like Lana?

"Why do you want to do that?" asked Lilly.

"Lana and her friends are always telling me what to do," said Shameeka. "But I'm just as good as they are. So I should try to become a cheerleader too!"

"That's true," said Lilly. "But if you become a cheerleader, you will have to support Lana's boyfriend, Josh Richter, when he plays at sports events. Do you want to do that?"

"Well," said Shameeka. "Cheerleading is an excellent way to keep fit and active. It's a mixture of two things I love—dancing and gymnastics. Also, if I become a cheerleader, it will look good when I apply for college."

"But if you join the cheerleading team," I asked, "will you stop eating lunch with us? Will you go and sit with the cheerleaders?"

I pointed across the cafeteria to a long table where Lana and Josh and the rest of the cheerleading team were having lunch. I felt very sad. I didn't want Shameeka to leave our little group.

52

"Of course not," said Shameeka. "If I become a cheerleader, my feelings for my friends aren't going to change. I'm not going to become a different person. I just won't be able to spend as much time with you as before."

We sat there thinking about Shameeka becoming a cheerleader. She would have to spend a lot of her free time doing dance practice with the team. I understood that this could be fun.

But why would anyone want to spend all that time with Lana Weinberger?

Thursday, January 21st. French class
My dad is wonderful.

My mom finally managed to speak to him in Genovia. She asked him if I had to go to the black-and-white ball on Friday. And my dad said no, I didn't have to go to the Contessa's party. He said that it was a stupid idea.

My dad said that the real reason Grandmere wants me to go to the ball is because she and the Contessa are rivals[43]. Grandmere thinks that she is better than the Contessa and the Contessa thinks that she is better than Grandmere. So Grandmere wants to show me off to the Contessa. The Contessa has a granddaughter too, but Grandmere wants to show her that I am better than the Contessa's granddaughter.

So I am free to spend tomorrow night with Michael! Everything is going to be all right, even though I have lost my lucky Queen Amidala underwear.

I am so happy.

9

Old Enemies

When I walked into Grandmere's suite at the Plaza Hotel today, I had a big shock.

Grandmere was sitting quietly in the dark. She looked terrible. Her hair wasn't brushed and she hadn't put on her make-up. She wasn't even drinking her favorite cocktail. She just sat there, with her dog, Rommel, on her knee.

"Grandmere," I cried out when I saw her. "Are you all right? Are you sick?"

"No," said Grandmere in a quiet voice. "I'm fine. Well, I will be fine. When I recover from the humiliation[44]."

"Humiliation? What humiliation?" I asked. I went over to kneel[45] by her chair. "Grandmere, are you sure you aren't sick? You aren't even smoking!"

"I'll be all right," she said weakly. "I'm strong. I'm a Renaldo. I will get better."

"Grandmere," I said. "Do you want me to call a doctor?"

"No doctor can cure my illness," said Grandmere. "I am suffering from humiliation because I have a granddaughter who doesn't love me."

I had no idea what Grandmere was talking about. It's true that I don't like her sometimes. Sometimes I even think I hate her. But I still love her.

"Grandmere," I said. "What are you talking about? Of course I love you."

"Then why won't you come with me to Contessa Trevanni's black-and-white ball?" cried Grandmere. "Your father says that you don't want to go."

"Grandmere," I said. "You know why I don't want to go. You know that Michael and I . . ."

"*That boy!*" cried Grandmere. "*That boy* again!"

"Grandmere, stop calling him that," I said. "You know his name. It's Michael."

"And I suppose this Michael," said Grandmere, "is more important to you than I am."

"Grandmere, tomorrow night is our first date," I said. "Mine and Michael's. It's really important to me."

"It was really important to me that you go to this ball," said Grandmere. "Since I was a little girl, Contessa Elena Trevanni has thought that she is better then me—just because her family was richer than my family. She always had nicer clothes and handbags and shoes than my parents could afford for me. Then she married a very rich man, so she doesn't have to work. But I have had to work hard helping to attract tourists to Genovia.

"So she still thinks she is better than me," Grandmere went on. "But this time, I was hoping that I could show her my lovely granddaughter."

I was very surprised. I had had no idea that this ball was so important to Grandmere. But now I realized something about Contessa Trevanni and Grandmere.

Contessa Trevanni was like Lana Weinberger. She behaved to Grandmere like Lana behaves towards me.

"And now," said Grandmere in a very sad voice, "I have to tell her that my granddaughter doesn't love me. She won't even give up her date with her new boyfriend for one night."

Suddenly I realized what I had to do. I understood how Grandmere felt about Contessa Trevanni because that was how I felt about Lana. Lana has been mean and cruel to me for a long time. Not only to me, but to all the girls at school who aren't good-looking.

But I hadn't known there was someone who treated Grandmere like that. I started feeling very sorry for her.

"All right, Grandmere," I said. "I'll go to your ball."

Immediately Grandmere looked brighter.

"Really, Amelia?" she said. She took my hand. "Will you really do this for me?"

I knew if I went to the ball, I would lose Michael forever. Michael was going to dump me because I had canceled our first date. And I am doing this for *Grandmere*, who I don't even like!

Suddenly Grandmere started looking very happy. She rang for her maid to bring her a cocktail and cigarettes. Then we started our princess lesson.

When am I going to tell Michael about the ball? I'll have to tell him tomorrow morning. Then he can dump me in Homeroom, before our Algebra lesson. Lana will be in Algebra and I don't want her to see me crying when he dumps me.

Thursday, January 21st. The Loft

Tina doesn't think Michael is going to dump me tomorrow. She says he isn't going to break up with me because he loves me. I said yes, he will, because he only loves me as a friend.

Maybe I can change to another school from the Albert Einstein High School. I don't think I can continue going to the same school as Michael if we break up. I don't think I can see him every day in the hallway between classes, at lunch and in our Special Project class.

But maybe no other school in Manhattan will want me.

Friday, January 22nd. Homeroom

Well. It's over. Michael dumped me.

He didn't exactly say he wanted to break up with me. But I could read his feelings in his face and his eyes.

"I understand, Mia," he said. "You're a princess. So the most important thing is your duty. You have to put your duty first."

But I'm sure he didn't mean that.

I told him that I would try and leave the ball early if I could. He said that if I did, I should call in at the Moscovitzes' apartment.

I know what this means, of course.

He's going to dump me there.

I cannot blame him. I would do the same thing.

I will, of course, give him his birthday present. I went to a lot of trouble to steal it. But I know it won't do any good. Michael and I are finished.

They have just announced the name of the newest member of the Albert Einstein High School cheerleading team. It's my friend, Shameeka Taylor.

But I'm so unhappy about Michael that I don't even care.

Friday, January 22nd. Algebra class

Michael didn't come into my Algebra class today to say "Hi" on his way to his English class.

I know why. We are broken up. He hates me now. I don't blame him. I hate myself.

Lana just turned around and said,

"Your friend is on the cheerleading team now. But that doesn't mean anything is going to change between us, Mia."

Then she turned around again. But she wasn't fast enough. Her long blonde hair was still lying across my Algebra book.

I closed my book sharply. Lana's hair was caught inside, and she screamed in pain.

Mr Gianini was at the front of the class, writing on the board. When he heard Lana scream, he turned around.

"Mia," he said in a tired voice. "Lana. What is the matter?"

"She closed her book on my hair," said Lana.

"I didn't know her hair was in my book," I told him.

Mr Gianini made me open my book again. But he didn't send me to the principal's office.

I felt very good because I had hurt Lana, my enemy. I almost forgot that I had a broken heart and that Michael is going to dump me after the black-and-white ball tonight.

Friday, January 22nd. Special Project class
At lunch today, everyone had a reason to be happy.

Shameeka was happy because she had got onto the cheerleading team.

Tina was happy because she had decided to forget Dave, but she wasn't going to stop reading romantic books.

Boris, Lilly's boyfriend, was happy because he is always happy.

But I don't know if Michael was happy or sad because he didn't come to lunch. He told me he had some things to do, and that he would see me in Special Project class.

Some things to do. Is he looking for another girl to take to the movie tonight?

Maybe I should just ask him. I should just say, *Look, are we broken up?* But I can't ask Michael right now because he is talking with Boris about music.

How can Michael talk about music while my heart is breaking?

Friday, January 22nd, 6 p.m., Grandmere's Suite at the Plaza

Grandmere made me come here straight after school. Paolo is here too. Paolo is a beauty stylist so he is helping us with our clothes and hair and make-up for the ball.

I look good. But inside I feel terrible. I'm trying not to show it. I want Grandmere to think I'm having a good time. I'm only going to the ball because of her. She is an old lady and my grandmother and I want to make her feel happy.

Well, it's time to go. Grandmere has a black dress on. My dress is white. Grandmere says I look like a snowdrop[46].

Maybe I've found my secret talent. Maybe my talent is to look like a snowdrop.

10

The Black-and-White Ball

Friday, January 22nd, 8 p.m., Bathroom at Contessa Trevanni's Mansion on Fifth Avenue

I'm in the bathroom again. I'm thinking about Grandmere.

Grandmere told me that she and Contessa Trevanni were old enemies, and I believed her. I felt sorry for her. But it was just a trick. Grandmere wanted me to come to the ball so that people would think I was PRINCE RENÉ'S NEW GIRLFRIEND!!!!!!!

I don't think that René knew what Grandmere was going to say. When Grandmere introduced me to Contessa Trevanni, he looked very surprised.

"Contessa, may I present to you my granddaughter, Princess Amelia Mignonette Grimaldi Renaldo," said Grandmere. Then she added, "And of course you know Amelia's boyfriend, Prince Pierre René Grimaldi Alberto."

Boyfriend? BOYFRIEND??? René and I looked at each other in surprise. Just then I noticed that Lana Weinberger and her dad, and her mom were standing RIGHT THERE BEHIND US.

I noticed Lana's mom had allowed her to wear a black dress to the ball. But Grandmere had told me I was too young to wear black. And Lana is the same age as me.

I knew that Lana had heard what Grandmere said about me and René. She had a very strange look on her face.

"So now Lana is going to tell everyone at school that I'm dating Michael *and* another boy," I thought.

René was looking amused but I was very angry.

"I can't believe you did that!" I cried, as soon as we were away from the Contessa. "You told that woman that René and I are going out. Grandmere, how many times do I have to tell you? I'm going out with Michael Moscovitz!"

"René," said Grandmere sweetly. "Please go and get us some champagne."

When René had gone, Grandmere said,

"Amelia. I was only trying to make René feel welcome. And what's wrong with him? He's very charming and handsome. How can you prefer a high school boy to a *prince*?"

"Because, Grandmere," I said. "I love Michael. I know you want me to marry Prince René because he's royal. But that isn't going to happen. Even if Michael and I broke up, I am *not* going to become René's girlfriend. He's not the kind of boy I like."

"All right," Grandmere said. "I will stop calling René your boyfriend. But you must dance with him. Just one time."

"Grandmere…" I said. I really didn't feel like dancing. "Please. Not tonight."

"Amelia," said Grandmere in a different kind of voice. "One dance. That's all I am asking for. I believe you *owe* me one dance with Prince René."

I started to laugh.

"Owe you?" I said. "What do you mean?"

"Because something was taken from the palace museum," said Grandmere. "A very valuable object. It was given to me by my dear friend, the former American President, Richard Nixon. Richard is now dead, of course, but when he was alive he helped Genovia a lot. But I suppose you don't know anything about this, do you, Amelia?"

I didn't know what to say. I felt very embarrassed. How had Grandmere found out that I had taken something from the palace museum? There was only one thing that I could do now.

"You know what, Grandmere?" I said. "I'll be happy to dance with Prince René."

"Good," said Grandmere, looking very happy.

So I was forced to dance with Prince René. While we were dancing, a strange thing happened. Suddenly René said,

"Who's that blonde girl who keeps staring at us? Do you know her?"

I looked over to see who he was talking about. Lana was dancing nearby with an older man. She didn't look very happy. She was giving me very jealous looks.

I suppose to Lana, I looked like I had everything. I looked like a snowdrop, and I was dancing with the most handsome guy at the ball.

Unfortunately, I was in love with someone else.

Suddenly I started feeling sorry for Lana. Until then, I had always thought of her as my enemy. But now I wanted to do something nice for her.

So I looked up at René and said,

"Yeah, I know her. Her name is Lana. She goes to my school. When this dance is over, you should ask her for the next dance. She'll be very excited about dancing with a handsome prince."

63

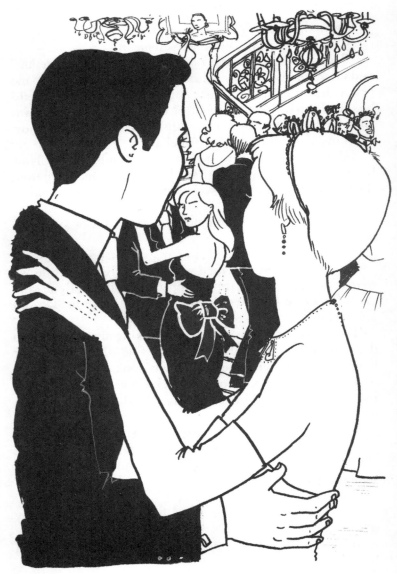

"Yeah, I know her. Her name is Lana. She goes to my school."

"But you're not excited about dancing with a prince," said René with a smile.

"René," I said. "I already met my prince, long before I met you. But if I don't leave this ball soon, I'm afraid he won't be my prince for much longer."

And that's why I'm in the bathroom. René said he would help me leave the ball. He told me to hide. Then he told Lars to go out and get a cab. While Grandmere is busy, René is going to knock on the door so I'll know I can leave. Later, René is going to explain to Grandmere that I felt sick, and so Lars took me home.

René's just knocked on the door. I have to go.

11

Michael's Birthday Present

Friday, January 22nd, 11 p.m., the Moscovitzes' Bathroom
I'm so happy. I don't think Michael is going to break up with me.

When Lars and I arrived at the Moscovitzes apartment, I rang the bell. We waited in the hall outside. I was still wearing my ball dress because there hadn't been time to go home and change.

Michael opened the door. He was surprised to see me in my white snowdrop dress.

"Oh, hey, come in, you look . . . you look really beautiful," Michael said. I went in and so did Lars. Then Lars went into the living-room to watch TV with Michael's mom and dad.

"Did you eat yet?" asked Michael. "Because I have some veggie burgers[47] . . ."

I looked at him in surprise. Do guys usually offer their girlfriends a veggie burger before they break up with them? I didn't know. But I didn't think so.

"Um," I said. "I don't know. If you're having one . . ."

So we went into the kitchen. Lilly was there.

"Hello," she said. "Why are you wearing that dress?"

"I was at a ball," I explained.

Michael started cooking. He took out two veggie burgers and heated them up. Then he put them on two pieces of bread, and put the bread on plates. He put everything on a tray and took it into the TV room.

I followed him. And there, on the TV screen, were the words *Star Wars*. It was the beginning of the movie.

"Michael," I said in surprise. "What is this?"

"Well," he said, "you couldn't go and see *Star Wars* at the

Screening Room tonight. So I've brought *Star Wars* to you. It's on a DVD."

"Wait a minute," I said. "You aren't breaking up with me? When I told you I couldn't go out with you tonight, you went very quiet. And you didn't have lunch with us."

"I was thinking about what we could do tonight," said Michael. "Then I had to order the veggie burgers and get the *Star Wars* DVD. That's why I wasn't at lunch."

"Oh," I said. "So you don't want to break up with me?"

"No," said Michael. "Mia, I love you, remember? Why would I want to break up with you?"

I felt wonderfully happy. But still, something wasn't right. There was one more question I had to ask.

"Do you just love me as a friend?" I asked. "Or are you *in* love with me?"

Michael was staring at me. I felt my face turn red. Then he took both my hands in his and gave me a really long kiss.

"Of course I'm in love with you," he said. "Now come and eat."

It was the most romantic moment of my whole life. I will never be as happy again. Michael Moscovitz is in love with me, Mia Thermopolis!

We sat there, eating our veggie burgers and watching *Star Wars*. Later, Michael went into the kitchen to get some ice-cream. While he was there, I put a small box on the table.

"What's this?" asked Michael when he came back.

"It's your birthday present," I said, feeling very excited.

"I told you that you didn't have to give me anything," said Michael, picking up the box.

"I know," I said. "But I saw this, and I thought it was perfect."

"Well," said Michael. "Thanks." He lifted the lid of the box. And there inside was a dirty little rock[48].

67

"It's . . . it's really nice," said Michael.

I laughed happily. "You don't know what it is! Can't you guess?"

"Well," he said again. "It looks like . . . I mean, it looks very much like a rock."

"It *is* a rock," I said. "Guess where it's from."

Michael looked at it. "I don't know. Genovia?" he asked.

"No," I said. "It's from the moon! It's a *moon* rock! From when Neil Armstrong[49] was there. He collected a lot of rocks, and Richard Nixon gave some to my grandmother when he was President. And I saw them in the museum in Genovia and I thought . . . well, that you should have one. I know you like things that are about outer space[50]."

Michael looked up. "Mia," he said, "I can't accept this."

"Yes, you can," I replied. "There are plenty more rocks back at the palace museum."

"Mia," said Michael. "It's a rock. From the moon. From two hundred and thirty-eight thousand miles away."

"Yes," I said. I wasn't sure what he meant. Didn't he like it?

I suppose it was weird to give your boyfriend a rock for his birthday. But it was a very special rock. And Michael was a very special boyfriend. I really thought he'd like it.

"Michael, if you don't like it, I can give it back . . ."

"No," he said, moving the box away from me. "I just don't know what I'm going to get you for your birthday. I can't think of anything as special as this."

So then we ate our ice-creams and watched the rest of the movie. I couldn't stop smiling. In fact, that's why I've locked myself in the bathroom. To try and calm down a little. I am so happy that it's difficult to write. I . . .

"It is a rock," I said. "Guess where it's from."

Saturday, January 23rd

I had to stop writing last night, because Lilly started banging on the bathroom door. She was trying to get in. When I opened it, she saw me with my journal and pen. Then she said,

"Have you been in here for the past half hour, writing in your journal?"

I admit that it is a little weird, but I was so happy, I had to write it down. Then I would never forget how I felt.

"And you still don't know what you're good at?" asked Lilly. When I shook my head, she went away, looking mad.

But I can't be mad with Lilly, because . . . well, I'm so in love with her brother.

I can't be mad with Grandmere either. She called me here at home a little while ago. She wanted to know if I was feeling better. My mom told her I was fine. So then Grandmere wanted to know if I could go and have tea with her and the Contessa. But I said that I was busy with homework.

And I can't be mad with René. He helped me a lot last night. I wonder how he and Lana got along. I wonder if she'll break up with Josh Richter and start going out with René.

And I have my special lucky Queen Amidala underwear back. Our neighbour had taken our bag of laundry from the hall by mistake. She went on vacation and has only just come back. So she didn't notice until now that she had the wrong bag of laundry.

Another wonderful thing happened last night. When Lilly walked away from the bathroom, Michael asked me what was wrong.

"Oh," I said, putting away my journal. "She's mad because I don't know what my secret talent is. You and Lilly are good at so many things, and I'm not good at anything."

"Mia," Michael said. "You have a great talent. You are very good at writing. Everyone knows you can write. And you always get 'A' grades for your papers in English."

I realized Michael was right. I am always writing in this journal. And I write a lot of poetry, and I write notes and emails. But I never thought that writing was my talent. It's just something I do all the time, like breathing.

Perhaps I can start writing lots of things for the Genovian parliament.

But first I'm going bowling with Michael and Lilly and Boris. Because even a princess has to have fun sometimes.

71

Points for Understanding

1

1 Why isn't Mia enjoying her visit to Genovia?
2 Where is Michael and why is Mia worried about him?
3 How does Tina help Mia?

2

1 What important day did Mia forget?
2 It is 3 o'clock in the morning in Genovia. What time is it in Florida?
3 Why doesn't Mia want to give Michael a sweater or candy?

3

1 What advice does Grandmere give Mia about Michael?
2 Why does she give Mia *Jane Eyre* to read?
3 What do Mia and Tina plan to do about their boyfriends?
4 What promise do they make to each other?

4

1 How does Mia feel when she gets back to New York?
2 Why is Mia's mom worried about *Jane Eyre*?
3 Why does Mia decide to phone Michael? What happens?

5

1 How does Mia feel the next morning?
2 Why is Mia's Queen Amidala underwear important to her?
3 Why does she feel depressed in the Special Project class?

6

1 What lie does Grandmere tell Principal Gupta?
2 Why does Grandmere take Mia to the *Chanel* shop?
3 What problem does Mia have about Friday?
4 Why doesn't she tell Michael the truth?

7

1 What mistake did Tina make with her boyfriend, Dave?
2 Why is Mia surprised when she goes for her princess lesson?
3 What does Mia think Grandmere is trying to do?
4 Who is taking Mia to the ball?

8

1 What job does Lana's father do? Why has Contessa
   Trevanni invited him and his family to the ball?
2 Why are Shameeka's friends surprised by her plan?
3 What are Grandmere's real reasons for wanting Mia to go
   to the ball?

9

1 Why is Mia shocked when she goes to visit Grandmere?
2 Why does Mia agree to go to the ball?
3 Do you think Michael is going to dump Mia? Why/why not?

10

1 Why does Mia think Lana is jealous of her?
2 What good thing does Mia do for Lana?
3 How does René help Mia?

11

1   How does Mia feel when she goes to see Michael?
2   In what two ways does Michael surprise Mia?
3   Why does Mia think Michael doesn't like his birthday
     present?
4   What is Mia's secret talent? How does she find out what
     it is?

Glossary

1 **algebra** (page 7)
   a type of mathematics that uses letters in place of numbers.
2 **stepfather** (page 7)
   someone's step father is their mother's new husband in a second or later marriage.
3 **pregnant** (page 7)
   if a woman is pregnant, she has a baby growing inside her body.
4 **cancer** (page 8)
   a serious illness caused by the cells in the body spreading in an uncontrolled way.
5 **chemotherapy** (page 8)
   the use of special drugs, often used to treat cancer.
6 **heir** (page 8)
   someone who will receive money, property or a title when another person dies.
7 **Dowager** (page 8)
   title of a woman who has money or property because her dead husband belonged to a high social class.
8 **cocktail** (page 8)
   a drink, usually with a lot of alcohol, made by mixing different drinks together.
9 **tan** (page 9)
   if you have a tan, the sun has made your skin a darker color.
10 **guy** (page 12)
   informal expression for a man or boy.
11 **relief** (page 14)
   a relaxed, happy feeling you get because something bad has not happened, or when a bad situation has ended.
12 **extension** (page 16)
   an extra telephone line connecting to a main line.
13 **handkerchief** (page 17)
   a small, square piece of cloth or paper used for wiping your nose or eyes.
14 **boxer shorts** (page 17)
   men's underwear that looks like a pair of short loose trousers.

15 **Jane Eyre** (page 18)
a love story written in 1846 by the British author, Charlotte Brontë, about the relationship between Jane Eyre, a poor young teacher, and her rich employer, Mr Rochester.

16 **ruin**—*to ruin* (page 18)
to destroy or badly damage something.

17 **realize**—*to realize* (page 18)
to know and understand something.

18 **mean** (page 20)
if you are mean to someone, you act towards them in a bad or cruel way.

19 **available** (page 20)
if you are *available* for someone in a romantic way, you are happy to become involved with them.

20 **ball** (page 21)
a formal social event with dancing and usually a meal.

21 **fix** (someone) **up** – *to fix (someone up)* (page 22)
if you *fix up* two people, you arrange a situation where they might begin a romantic relationship.

22 **fall** (page 23)
the season between summer and winter. British autumn.

23 **Manhattan** (page 24)
the island that is the main cultural and business center of New York City.

24 **kidnap**—*to kidnap* (page 24)
to take someone away and make them a prisoner, usually because you want their family or government to give you money or make them do what you want.

25 **loft** (page 25)
room at the top of a building, under the roof.

26 **grabbed**—*to grab* (page 27)
to take hold of something in a rough or rude way.

27 **brilliant** (page 28)
a *brilliant* idea is an idea that is extremely good.

28 **jetlagged** (page 30)
feeling very tired and confused because you have travelled quickly on a plane across parts of the world where the time is different.

29 **heroine** (page 30)
the main female character in a book, film or play.

30 **Special Project class** (page 32)
a class where students can work on the subjects that most interest them, or that they are most good at.

31 *depressed* (page 33)
if you are depressed, you feel very sad and unhappy.

32 *talent* (page 34)
being good at a particular activity, like music or dance.

33 *limousine* (page 36)
a large, expensive and comfortable car.

34 *Homeroom* (page 36)
a place where students go at the beginning of each school day and the teacher checks which students are not in school.

35 *Contessa* (page 38)
Italian for "Countess"—the title for a woman who is the wife of a count, a European nobleman.

36 *duty* (page 40)
if you do your duty, you do what is right or expected from someone in your position.

37 *escort* (page 46)
a person who goes with someone to a formal social event as their partner.

38 **break up (with)** – *to break up (with)* (page 47)
to end a romantic relationship or marriage.

39 *dump*—*to dump* (page 48)
informal expression meaning to end a romantic relationship with someone.

40 *laundry* (page 50)
(a) dirty clothes that you are washing or (b) a business that washes and irons clothes.

41 *operation* (page 51)
cutting into someone's body for medical reasons.

42 *cheerleader* (page 52)
one of a group of people, especially young women, who shout and dance to encourage the crowd at a sports event.

43 *rivals*
a person, team or business that competes with another.

44 *humiliation* (page 54)
a feeling of being unhappy and ashamed when something embarrassing happens.

45 **kneel**—*to kneel* (page 54)

to put both knees on the ground.

46 **snowdrop** (page 60)

a small, white flower that appears in early spring.

47 **veggie burger** (page 66)

pieces of vegetable pressed together in a flat round shape and served in a bread roll.

48 **rock** (page 67)

a piece of stone.

49 **Neil Armstrong** (page 68)

American astronaut—first man on the moon in July 1969.

50 **outer space** (page 68)

the area around the Earth containing stars and planets.

Dictionary extracts adapted from the Macmillan English Dictionary © Bloomsbury Publishing PLC 2002 and © A & C Black Publishers Ltd 2005

Exercises

Vocabulary: meanings of words from the story

Put the words and phrases in the box next to the correct definitions.

> pregnant   tan   guy   realize   relief   extension   ruin
> mean   available   stepfather   ball   kidnap   jetlag   heroine
> depressed   talent   escort   rival   humiliation   dump

1		(parental relationship to children) a man who marries a woman who already has children from an earlier marriage
2		(of a woman) expecting a baby
3		a light brown colour; the colour of a white person's skin after being in the sun for a long time
4		informal expression for a man or boy
5		to know and understand something (often suddenly)
6		a relaxed feeling when something bad has ended
7		an extra telephone line connected to a main line
8		to badly damage or destroy something
9		to behave in a bad or cruel way towards someone
10		be present and able to do something
11		a formal social event with dancing and usually food
12		to take someone prisoner and demand money for their release

13		a feeling of tiredness after a long plane journey – caused by the difference between time zones
14		the main female character in a book, film or play
15		to be very sad and unhappy
16		a special ability for music, mathematics etc.
17		a person who goes with another person to a formal social event – a partner
18		to throw away; an informal expression meaning to end a relationship with someone
19		a person who competes with another person (not as strong as an *enemy*)
20		a feeling of being unhappy and ashamed when something embarrassing happens

Writing: rewrite sentences

Rewrite the sentences using words and phrases in the previous exercise to replace the underlined words.

Example: My Mum is <u>expecting a baby</u>.
You write: *My Mum is pregnant.*

1 <u>Lana's face was brown</u> when she came back from Florida.
   Lana had

2 My mother married again, so Mr Gianini is <u>not my real father.</u>
   Mr Gianini

3 I didn't <u>know</u> how much I liked Michael until we were apart.
   I didn't

4 It was a <u>good feeling</u> to know that Michael hadn't forgotten me.

   It was

5 When I talked to Michael, Grandmere was listening on the <u>other line</u>.

   Grandmere

6 I think Grandmere wants to <u>destroy</u> my life.

   I think

7 I thought that Dave's text message to Tina was really <u>cruel</u>.

   I thought

8 I felt <u>really tired</u> after landing in New York.

   I felt

9 Jane Eyre is the <u>main character</u> in Charlotte Brontë's novel.

   Jane Eyre is

10 René will <u>accompany</u> me to the Contessa's party.

   René will

11 Lana and I were <u>always competing for his attention</u>.

   Lana and I

12 Grandmere said that my absence was a <u>great shame and embarrassment</u> to her.

   Grandmere said

13 I tried to call Michael, but <u>he was in class</u>.

   I tried to call Michael, but he

14 I don't have any special <u>ability</u> for algebra.

   I don't have

Vocabulary: anagrams

The letters of each word are mixed up. Write the words correctly.
The first one is an example.

Example:
HEROMEPATCHY special treatment for cancer using drugs
Chemotherapy

1	TANGPERN	She's going to be a mother
2	TRYPOPER	Land, buildings and goods that a person owns
3	HANDBUS	When a man is married to a woman he is called this
4	SIXREPESON	A fixed word or phrase – often used in an informal way
5	WARNDUREE	Clothing that you wear next to your skin
6	RELEMPOY	The person or company that you work for
7	CANROTIM	Connected with feelings of love and adventure
8	REPSIRON	A person in prison, or a person who is not free (at liberty)
9	BARG	Take something quickly and rudely
10	ROLFAM	Official or ceremonial; the opposite of casual
11	TEVEN	Something that happens
12	PATHIRONSIEL	The way in which two or more things or people are connected

13	DECALHEERER	One of a group of young women who shout and dance at a sports event to encourage the players
14	KENEL	To put both knees on the ground
15	RUST APEECO	Anywhere outside the Earth's atmosphere

Word Focus: *available*

Available means something that can be found or used or someone who is free to do something.

Rewrite the sentences using the word *available*. The first one is an example.

> **Example:** You can't have any pens. We've run out.
> You write: *There aren't any pens available.*

1 We will have some pens next week.
   Pens

2 How many members of staff are free to help with this project?
   How many members of staff

3 Grandmere hoped that Prince William might be free and able to marry Mia.
   Grandmere hoped that Prince William

Word Focus: *mean*

Mean has several different meanings. For example, as an adjective it is similar to the words *cruel* and *unkind*.
They were very cruel to their pets.

As a verb it can be used in a similar way to the verb *intend* or to refer to the meaning of a word.
She didn't mean to hurt him.
The word 'clever' means intelligent or smart.

Rewrite the sentences using the word *mean*. The first one is an example.

Example:	He is not a generous man.
You write:	*He is a mean man.*

1 I didn't intend to do it. It was an accident.
   I didn't

2 What is the French word *chic* in English?
   What does

3 Black clouds in the sky are usually a sign of rain.
   Black clouds in the sky

4 The average annual rainfall in New York is 47 inches.
   The

5 He said a lot of cruel things to her.
   He said

Word Focus: *suppose*

The verb *suppose* is used to mean that something is probably true/possible/going to happen.
I suppose the hero will marry the princess.

The structure *be supposed to* means to be expected to behave in a particular way.
I am supposed to go to the ball on Friday.

Rewrite the sentences using the word *suppose*. The first one is an example.

Example:	I guess it will rain.
You write:	*I suppose it will rain.*

1   I think I should take an umbrella.

2   I imagine that Lana will be jealous.

3   You should be at school.

4   You are late. You are meant to be at work before 9 am.

5   I think I should do some studying for tomorrow's test.

6   What are you doing here? You are meant to be at the ball.

Vocabulary Choice: words which are related in meaning

Which word is most closely related? Look at the example and circle the word which is most closely related to the word in bold.

Example: diary	milk-product	(journal)	cowshed	illness
1 **online**	straight	flying	live	in order
2 **instant**	timely	coffee	late	immediate
3 **break**	gear	feel	stop	vacation
4 **single**	only	double	music	married
5 **mad**	built	angry	cleaner	spoilt
6 **dial**	sun	call	email	stand
7 **trip**	journey	food	season	candy
8 **character**	book	person	litter	writer
9 **chase**	imitate	search	follow	fall

Vocabulary: opposite meanings

Look at the example. Circle the word which is nearest to the opposite meaning.

Example: everything	all	always	never	(nothing)
1 **available**	ready	free	obtainable	absent
2 **damage**	ruin	repair	destroy	spoil
3 **worried**	anxious	nervous	afraid	relaxed
4 **refuse**	agree	rubbish	reject	garbage
5 **awake**	alert	conscious	asleep	aware
6 **wonderful**	terrible	perfect	superb	great
7 **rude**	rough	polite	boring	vulgar
8 **special**	particular	exceptional	ordinary	unusual

86

Published by Macmillan Heinemann ELT
Between Towns Road, Oxford OX4 3PP
Macmillan Heinemann ELT is an imprint of
Macmillan Publishers Limited
Companies and representatives throughout the world
Heinemann is a registered trademark of Harcourt Education, used under licence.

EAN 978–1–4050–8718–6

This version of *The Princess Diaries: Mia Goes Forth* by Meg Cabot.
© Copyright Meg Cabot 2002

First published 2001 by HarperCollins Children's Books, USA a division of
HarperCollinsPublishers. First published in UK by Macmillan Children's
Books, a division of Macmillan Publishers Limited

*Meggin Cabot asserts her right to be identified as the author of the
original work of which this Graded Reader is an adaptation*

This retold version by Anne Collins for Macmillan Readers
Text © Macmillan Publishers Limited 2007
Design and illustration © Macmillan Publishers Limited 2007

This version first published 2007

Illustrated by Karen Donnelly
Cover illustration by Nicola Slater

Printed and bound in Thailand
2011 2010 2009 2008 2007

10 9 8 7 6 5 4 3 2 1